SAID
NO
NURSE
EVER

A COLORING BOOK
FOR NURSES WHO'VE SEEN IT ALL

Compiled by Jim Erskine
Select illustrations by Jess Erskine

www.RollingDonutPress.com

DEDICATED TO NURSES EVERYWHERE—
WE THANK YOU.

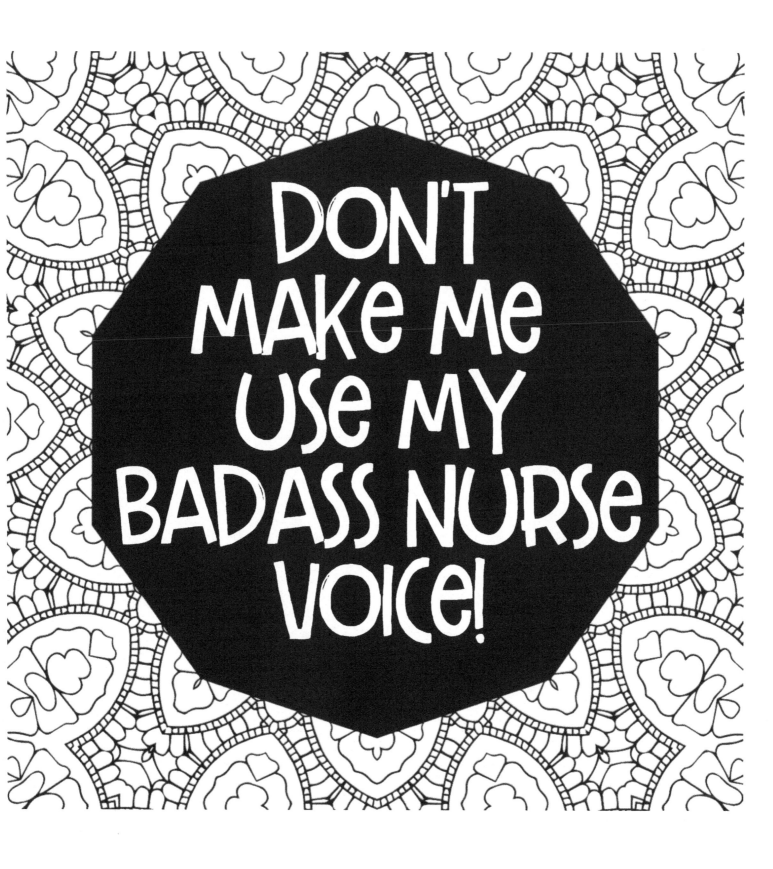

"I don't need a break" ...said no nurse, ever.

No,
I don't need any more coffee

...said no nurse, ever.

I LOVE
THE SMELL
OF DIARRHEA
IN THE MORNING...
SAID NO NURSE,
EVER.

CERTAINLY,

YOU MAY BORROW

MY BEST PEN...

SAID NO NURSE,

EVER

I LOVE MY LEISURELY, RELAXED LUNCH BREAK

...SAID NO NURSE, EVER.

SILENT NIGHT, HOLY NIGHT, ALL IS CALM

⭐

... SAID NO NIGHT SHIFT NURSE, EVER

HOORAY! I GET TO TAKE CARE OF THE
CONFUSED OLD NAKED GUY TODAY!
...SAID NO NURSE, EVER.

"I love when I start my shift and my patients fuss at me about everything that happened before I got there," said no nurse, ever.

"I love charting and writing long narrative nursing notes.. especially just before shift change," said no nurse, ever.

I LOVE
WHEN MY FAMILY
& FRIENDS CALL OR
TEXT ME FOR MEDICAL
ADVICE WHEN I'M
NOT AT WORK...
SAID NO NURSE,
EVER.

"I KNOW I LOOK CALM
AND PROFESSIONAL
TO YOU, BUT IN MY
IMAGINATION I'VE
ALREADY KILLED YOU
THREE TIMES,"

SAID NO NURSE, EVER.

I USE EVERYTHING I LEARNED IN NURSING SCHOOL PRETTY MUCH ON A DAILY BASIS... SAID NO NURSE EVER

I BECAME A NURSE FOR THE FAME AND THE MONEY ...SAID NO NURSE, EVER.

May your cup runneth over... except for that urine specimen cup you're trying to hand me

IT'S SO INVIGORATING WHEN THE SHIT HITS THE FAN AT SHIFT CHANGE... SAID NO NURSE, EVER.

"I love my soft, manicured hands that have gone to places I never thought possible," said no nurse, ever.

"GEE, THESE SCRUBS ARE SURE COZY & WARM,"

SAID NO NURSE, EVER.

"LIVING THE DREAM"

...SAID NO NIGHT SHIFT NURSE, EVER.

I'M LOOKING FORWARD TO ADJUSTING MY SLEEP SCHEDULE FOR NIGHT SHIFT...

...SAID NO NURSE, EVER.

"I CAN GO
FOR DAYS NOT
TALKING ABOUT
BOWELS
AND OTHER
GROSS SHIT,"
SAID NO
NURSE, EVER.

"PLEASE GIVE ME YOUR MOST CONFUSED PATIENTS WHEN I FLOAT TO YOUR FLOOR," SAID NO NURSE, EVER.

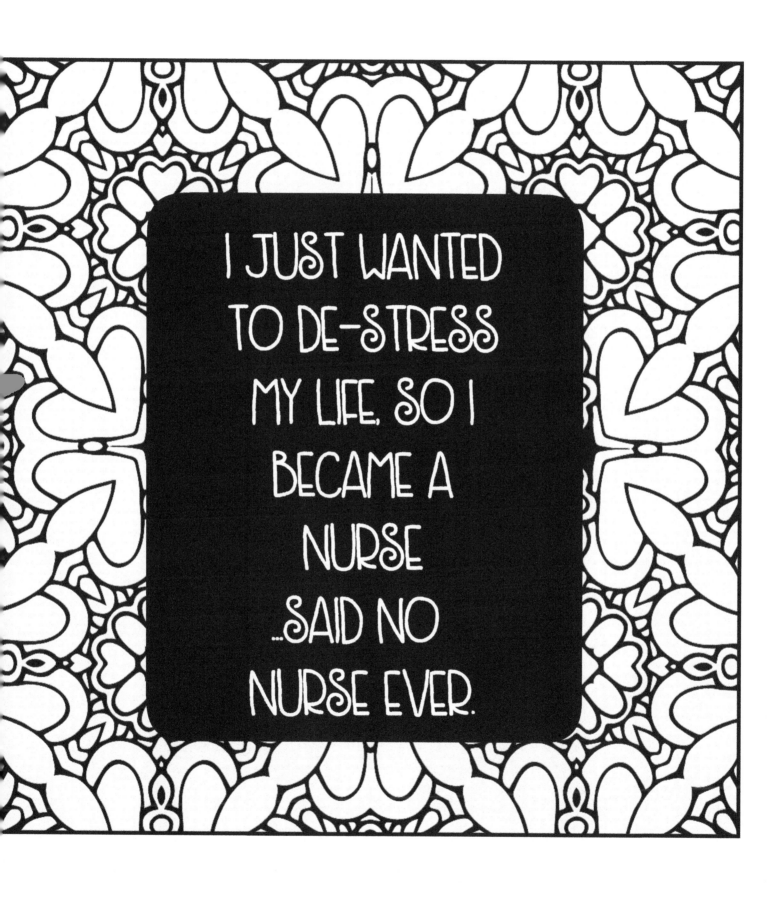

GEE,
I DIDN'T REALIZE
TOMORROW IS
MY DAY OFF...
SAID NO NURSE
EVER.

I WISH I COULD WORK MORE WEEKENDS

& HOLIDAYS

...SAID NO NURSE, ever.

"SURE YOU CAN GET OUT OF BED ALONE . THE TELEMETRY. FOLEY. OXYGEN AND IVs WILL BE JUST FINE" ...SAID NO NURSE. EVER.

"AFTER THAT REFRESHING 3 HOURS OF SLEEP LAST NIGHT, I'M PSYCHED FOR ANOTHER WONDERFUL SHIFT," SAID NO NURSE EVER.

I'VE SEEN IT, HEARD IT,
SMELLED IT, TOUCHED IT,
STEPPED IN IT, AND WORN IT...
SAID EVERY NURSE, EVER.

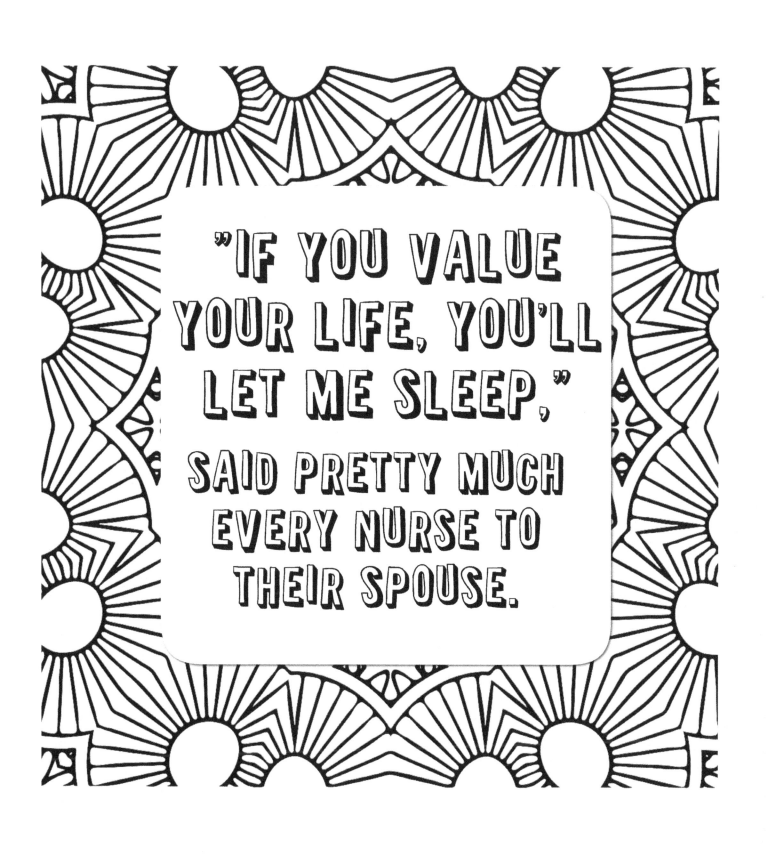

For more great titles visit:
www.RollingDonutPress.com

Rolling Donut Press

Made in the USA
Coppell, TX
20 October 2020